# First S

## Developing Lite........

## for 4 - 5 year olds

*Compiled by*

**D C Perkins**, BA (Hons), MEd, PhD (Wales) and **E J Perkins**, BSc (Hons), MEd

Design and Illustration **Anthony James**

Educational Adviser **Alison John, BEd**

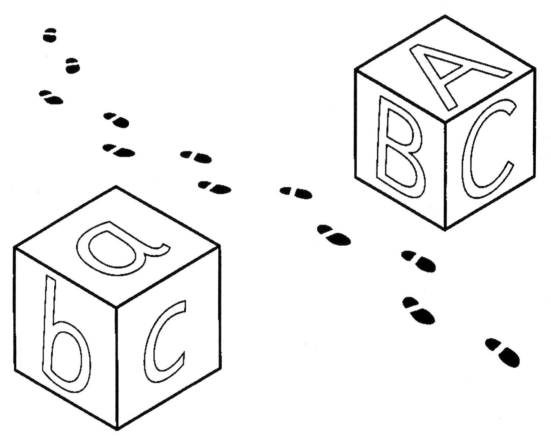

## DOMINO BOOKS (WALES) LTD

### SWANSEA SA1 1 FN

### Tel. 01792 459378   Fax. 01792 466337

### www.dominobooks.co.uk     email: sales@dominobooks.co.uk

First Steps Developing Literacy Skills © EJP & DCP 1999.

Reprinted 2000, 2001

ISBN 1 85772 151 9

# Contents

Page

CONTENTS TEACHERS' NOTES See next page

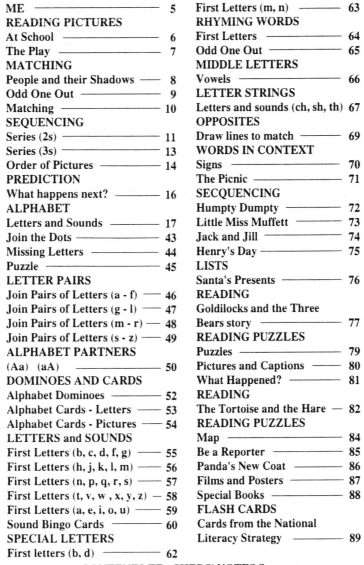

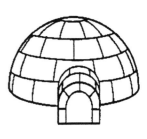

# Contents

## Teachers' Notes

# HOW TO USE THIS BOOK

For many experienced teachers the following few lines will seem superfluous.

The work in this book has been planned with the concepts underlying the *Desirable Outcomes for Children's Learning (SCAA)* **and the** *National Literacy Strategy* in mind. The book is based upon the requirements of the **National Curriculum, Key Stage 1.** Obviously, the ways in which the worksheets are used depend on the age, ability and experience of the children and the resources available. We do not envisage any problems choosing appropriate material.

1. All the material in this book is photocopiable as defined on the first page. This means that all the material can be used in any way you wish. Drawings can be photocopied and adapted for further work.

2. Covering sections of the master copies with plain paper enables resource material to be used in different ways. This is useful when it is felt that the material on one sheet should be used at different times especially with children who are slower at learning.

3. Some pages have two tests. It is a matter of choice whether both are done as part of the same session or done separately.

4. The master copies can be enlarged to A3 making it easier for several children to work on them at the same time.

5. Some of the photocopies can be cut to make additional puzzles and games.

6. At all stages encourage the children to colour their work. This develops motor skills, makes the completed work more interesting and often helps children grasp the meaning of the material.

7. Much of the completed work may be used as visual aids around the classroom.
Children feel pride when their work is 'pinned up'. It is important that each child's work should be 'exhibited' as often as possible. As well as encouraging them to produce their best, presentation of work in this way enables parents to keep in touch with what is happening and to assess the progress of their chidlren..

8. Remember there are often several ways in which problems can be tackled. Suggestions from children and the exchange of ideas should be encouraged. Learning to put forward ideas and to listen to the ideas of others are invaluable skills. Encourage the development of leaders but make sure that all take part. An incorrect answer can often be useful because it shows how material has been understood or mis-understood by children. It also shows how the rules and structure of language are being learned or naturally 'absorbed'.

9. Activities leading to logical thinking are invaluable. Teaching children to question material presented to them, to plan their work, to hypothesise and then to test their theories are skills that will help them in their everyday lives and when they are grown up.

It is important to keep the activities within the ability and the stage of development of the individual child. Moving too fast, unintentionally trying to do too much or extending the material too far may cause confusion and fear. As well, we have all met the bright child who becomes bored and frustrated because he/she is not able to go fast enough. No one said teaching was easy.

This is a drawing of me.

Me

My name is _____ I am ____ years old

Name _____

**At School**

Ahmed

Jane

Anne

Lee

John

How many children are in the picture? _____

What is Jane doing? _____

Who is painting? _____

What is Lee doing? _____

Who is under the table? _____

Draw your classroom or playroom. What are you doing?.

Name _____

## The Play

What is the name of the school play?

_____

What do the dwarfs do? _____

Who looks after them? _____

What happens to S _____ W _____? _____

_____

Name _____

Match the people and their shadows.

Name _____

Circle the odd one out in each set.

Name _____

Colour the things which match the first one in each row.

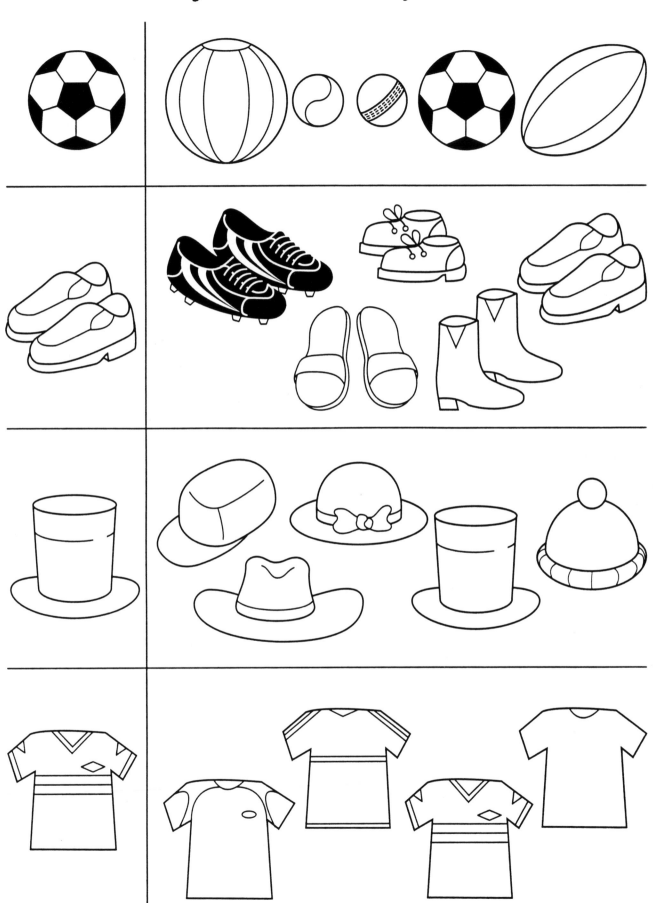

Name _____

Circle the one that comes next.

Name _____

## Circle the one that comes next.

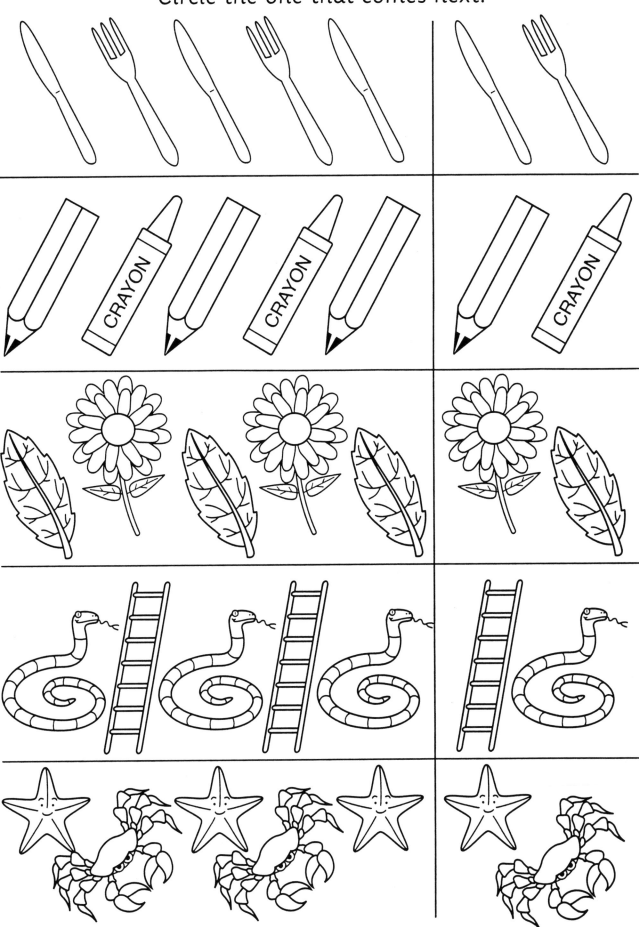

Name _____

## Circle the one that comes next.

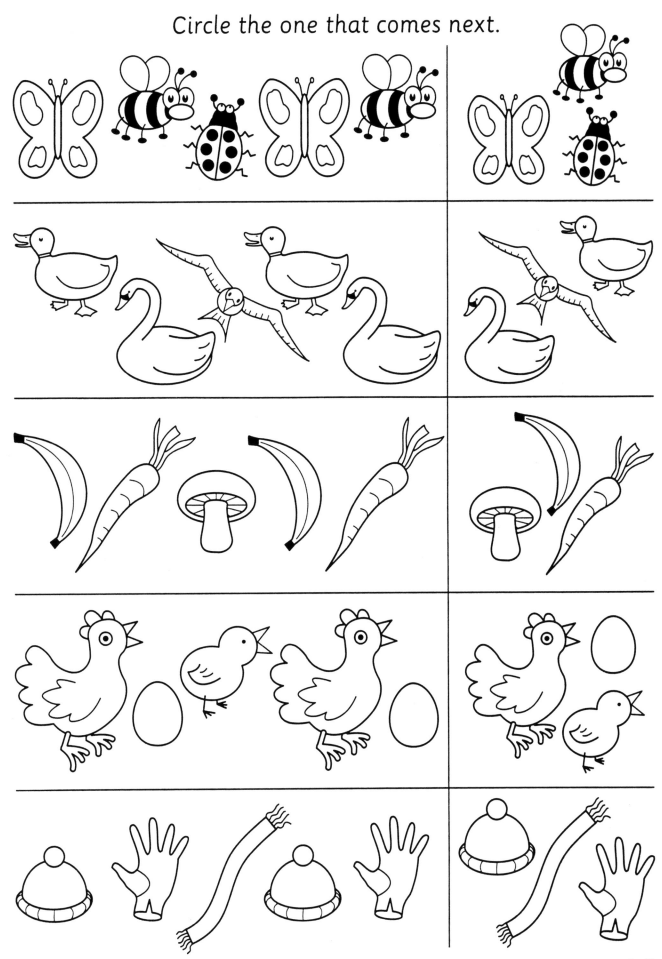

Name _____

Tick the picture that comes first.

Name _____

Tick the picture that comes first.

Name _____

What happens next?

Trace the letters. Colour the pictures that begin with the sound of a.

Follow the paths first with your finger and then with a pencil.

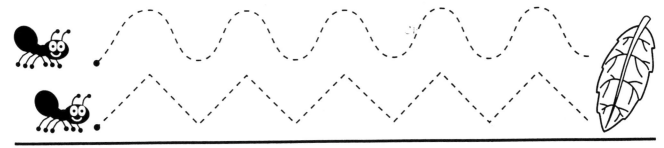

Trace and copy the letters.

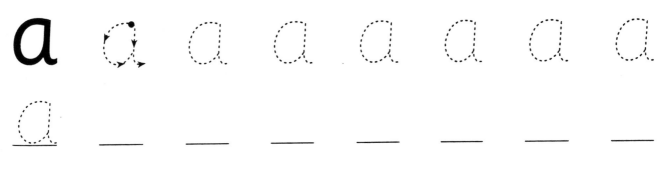

Finish the words and say them.

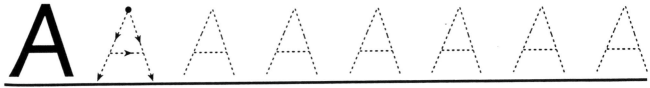

\_nt          \_\_xe          \_rrow          \_nchor

Trace the letters. Colour the pictures that begin with the sound of b.

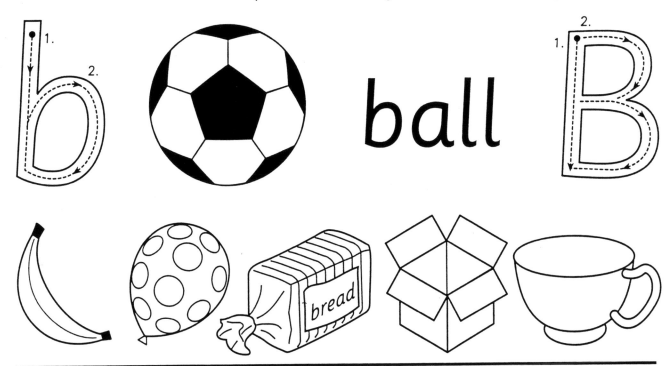

ball

Follow the paths first with your finger and then with a pencil.

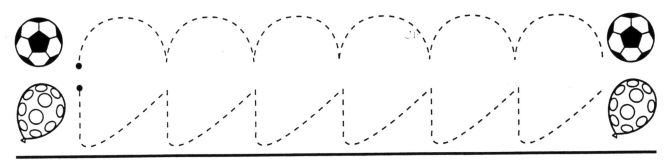

Trace and copy the letters.

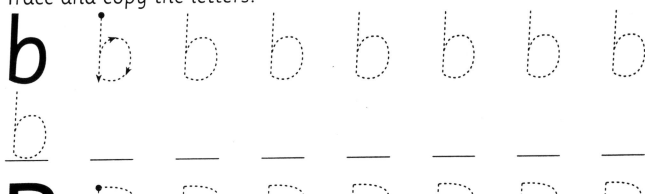

Finish the words and say them.

_all     _ox     _anana     _alloon

Trace the letters. Colour the pictures that begin with the sound of c.

C clown C

Join the dots. Colour the clowns' faces.

Trace and copy the letters.

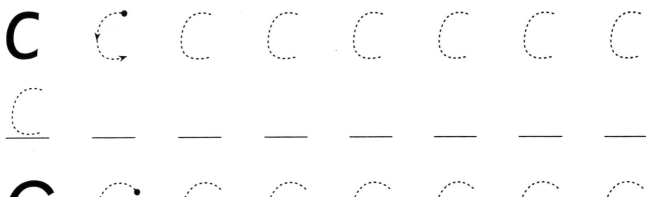

Finish the words and say them.

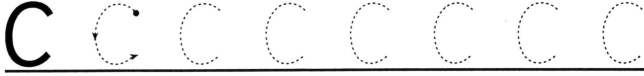

_ow          _ at          _oat          _racker

Trace the letters. Colour the pictures that begin with the sound of d.

d  duck  D

Follow the paths first with your finger and then with a pencil.

quack

Trace and copy the letters.

d d d d d d d d

d — — — — — — —

D D D D D D D D

Finish the words and say them.

_olphin      _og      _oor      _inosaur

Trace the letters. Colour the pictures that begin with the sound of e.

e   eskimo E

Join the dots and help the eskimo find his way home.

Trace and copy the letters.

e   e e e e e e e

e _ _ _ _ _ _ _ _

E E E E E E E E

Finish the words and say them.

_gg   _skimo   _lbow   _lephant

Trace the letters. Colour the pictures that begin with the sound of f.

Follow the path first with your finger and then with a pencil.

Trace and copy the letters.

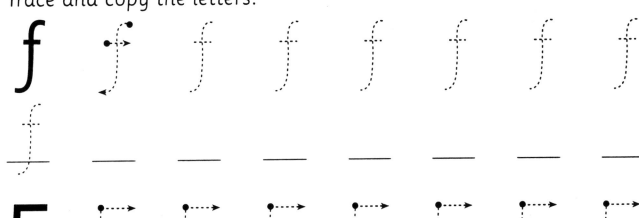

Finish the words and say them.

_ox          _airy          _lag          _ork

Trace the letters. Colour the pictures that begin with the sound of g.

gorilla

Follow the path first with your finger and then with a pencil.

Trace and copy the letters.

g g g g g g g g

g _ _ _ _ _ _ _

G G G G G G G G

Finish the words and say them.

_ love        _ate        _oat        _oal

Trace the letters. Colour the pictures that begin with the sound of h.

Follow the path first with your finger and then with a pencil.

Trace and copy the letters.

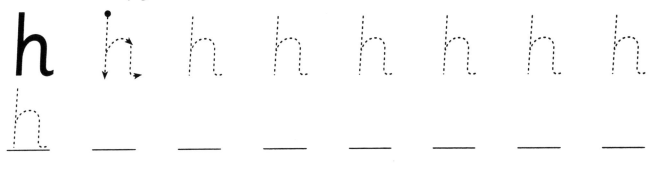

Finish the words and say them.

_ eart          _at          _orse          _edgehog

Trace the letters. Colour the pictures that begin with the sound of i.

*igloo*

Follow the path first with your finger and then with a pencil.

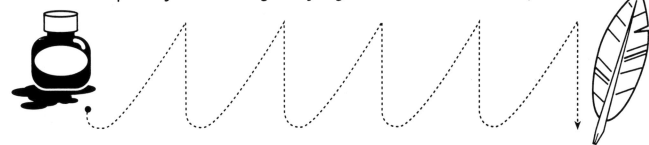

Trace and copy the letters.

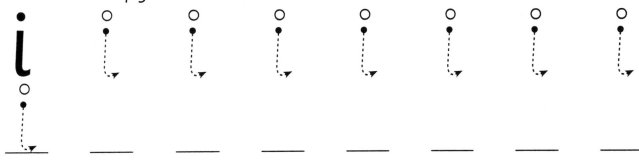

Finish the words and say them.

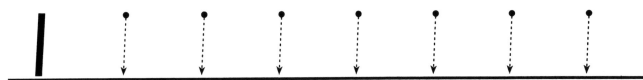

_ ndian          _ nk          _ gloo          _ tch

Trace the letters. Colour the pictures that begin with the sound of j.

Jeep

Follow the path first with your finger and then with a pencil.

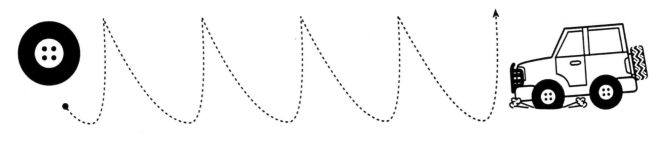

Trace and copy the letters.

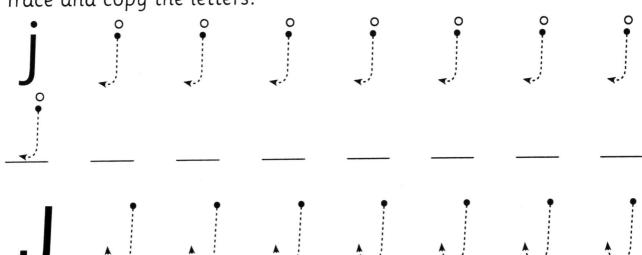

Finish the words and say them.

_umper        _am        _elly        _ug

Trace the letters. Colour the pictures that begin with the sound of k.

kangaroo

Follow the path first with your finger and then with a pencil.

Trace and copy the letters.

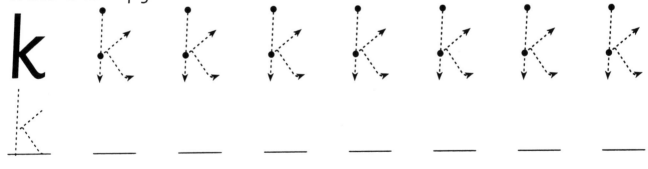

Finish the words and say them.

_ettle          _ing          _ite          _oala

Trace the letters. Colour the pictures that begin with the sound of l.

Follow the path first with your finger and then with a pencil.

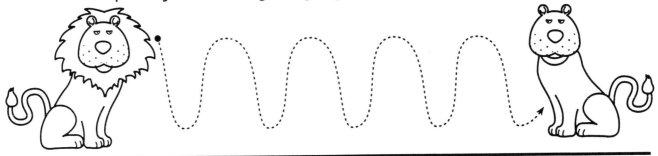

Trace and copy the letters.

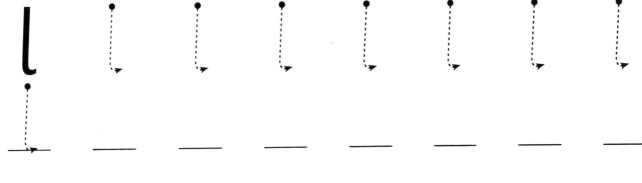

Finish the words and say them.

_ollypop      _eg      _og      _adybird

Trace the letters. Colour the pictures that begin with the sound of m.

moon

Follow the path first with your finger and then with a pencil.

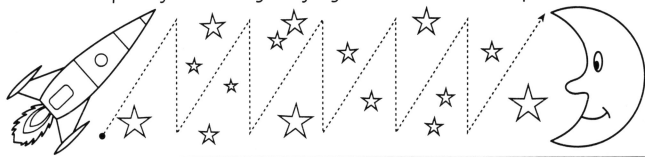

Trace and copy the letters.

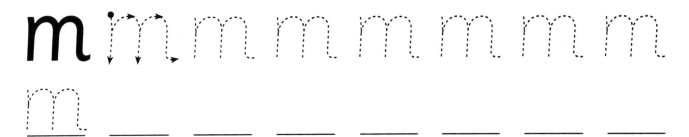

Finish the words and say them.

_onkey          _ug          _an          _ilk

Trace the letters. Colour the pictures that begin with the sound of n.

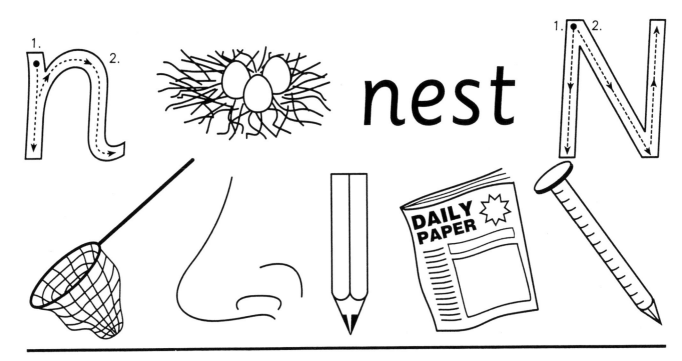

Follow the path first with your finger and then with a pencil.

Trace and copy the letters.

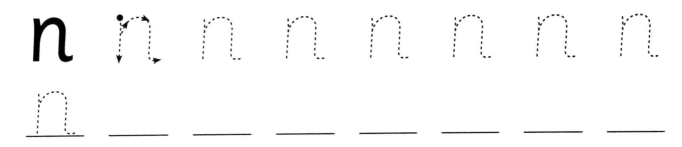

Finish the words and say them.

_ewspaper      _et      _ail      _ose

Trace the letters. Colour the pictures that begin with the sound of o.

orange

Follow the path first with your finger and then with a pencil.

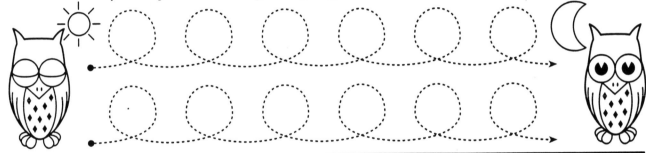

Trace and copy the letters.

Finish the words and say them.

_ctopus        _ar        _strich        _wl

Trace the letters. Colour the pictures that begin with the sound of p.

panda

Follow the path first with your finger and then with a pencil.

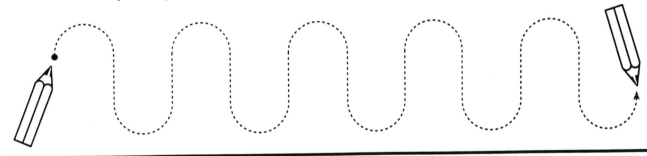

Trace and copy the letters.

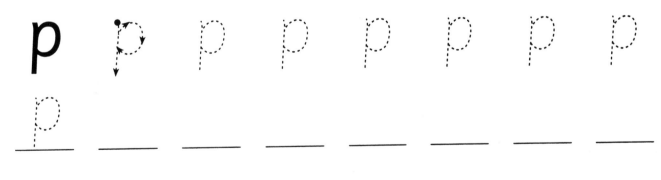

Finish the words and say them.

_enguin        _en        _encil        _eg

Trace the letters. Colour the pictures that begin with the sound of q.

Follow the path first with your finger and then with a pencil.

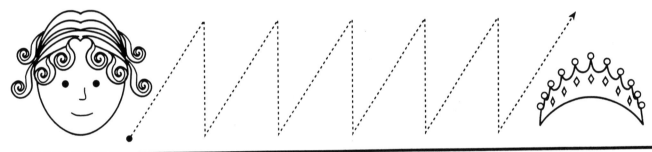

Trace and copy the letters.

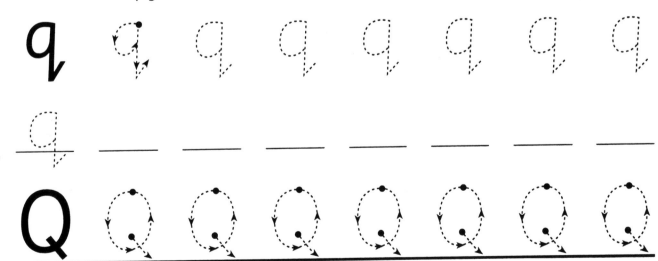

Finish the words and say them.

_ uilt       _ uill       _ uack       _ ueue

Trace the letters. Colour the pictures that begin with the sound of r.

rabbit

Follow the path first with your finger and then with a pencil.

Trace and copy the letters.

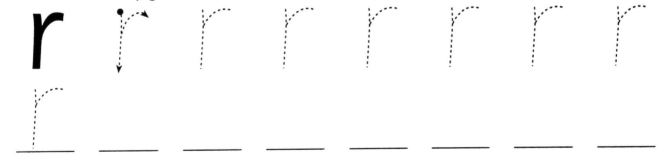

Finish the words and say them.

_ocket        _obot        _ainbow        _ing

Trace the letters. Colour the pictures that begin with the sound of s.

Follow the path first with your finger and then with a pencil.

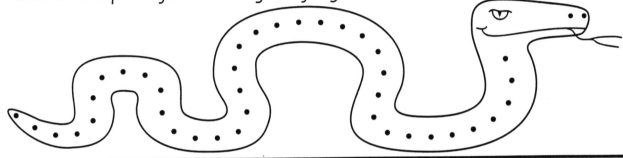

Trace and copy the letters.

S  S  S  S  S  S  S  S  S

S — — — — — — — —

S  S  S  S  S  S  S  S  S

Finish the words and say them.

_poon      _nake      _tar      _un

Trace the letters. Colour the pictures that begin with the sound of t.

teapot

The End

Follow the path first with your finger and then with a pencil.

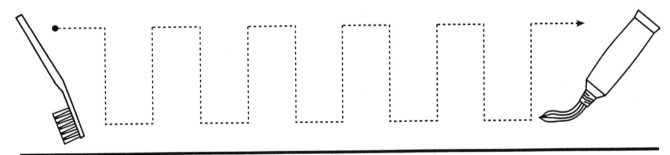

Trace and copy the letters.

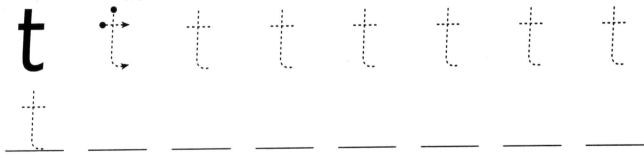

Finish the words and say them.

_elevision  _omato  _ap  _oothbrush

Trace the letters. Colour the pictures that begin with the sound of u.

umbrella

Follow the path first with your finger and then with a pencil.

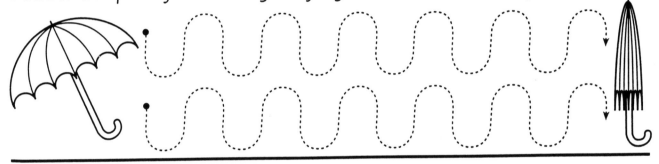

Trace and copy the letters.

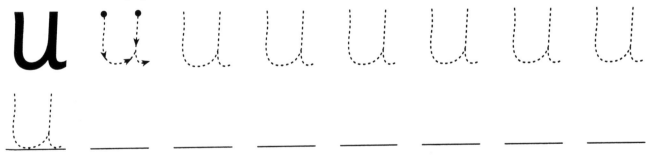

Finish the words and say them.

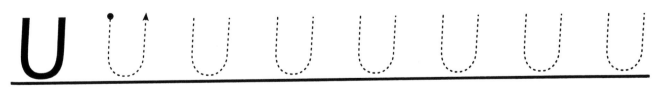

_pstairs    _dder    _nder    _mbrella

Trace the letters. Colour the pictures that begin with the sound of v.

van

Follow the path first with your finger and then with a pencil.

Trace and copy the letters.

Finish the words and say them.

_iolin        _est        _ase        _olcano

Trace the letters. Colour the pictures that begin with the sound of w.

whale

Follow the path first with your finger and then with a pencil.

Trace and copy the letters.

Finish the words and say them.

_ and          _ eb          _ itch          _ indow

Trace the letters. Colour the pictures that have the sound of x.

x-ray

Follow each shape with a pencil.

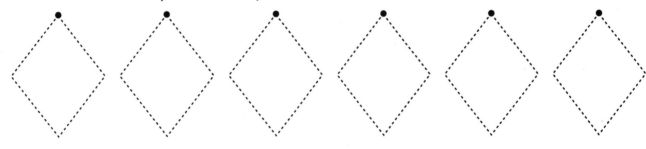

Trace and copy the letters.

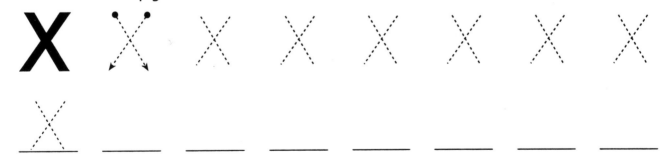

Finish the words and say them.

fo_          bo_          a_e          si_

Trace the letters. Colour the pictures that begin with the sound of y.

yacht

Follow the paths first with your finger and then with a pencil .

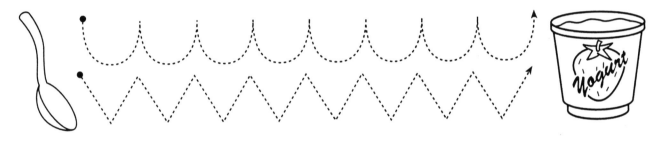

Trace and copy the letters.

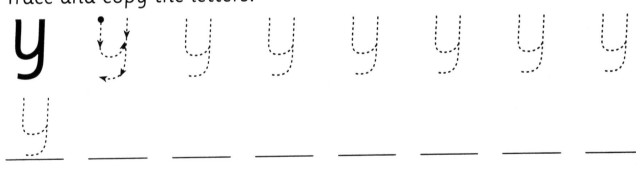

Finish the words and say them.

___awn      ___o-___o      ___ogurt      ___ellow

Trace the letters. Colour the pictures that begin with the sound of z.

zebra

Follow the paths first with your finger and then with a pencil .

Trace and copy the letters.

Z Z Z Z Z Z Z Z

Z ____

Z Z Z Z Z Z Z

Finish the words and say them.

_ip          _ebra          _ig-_ag          _oo

# Name _____

## Join the dots to finish the pictures.

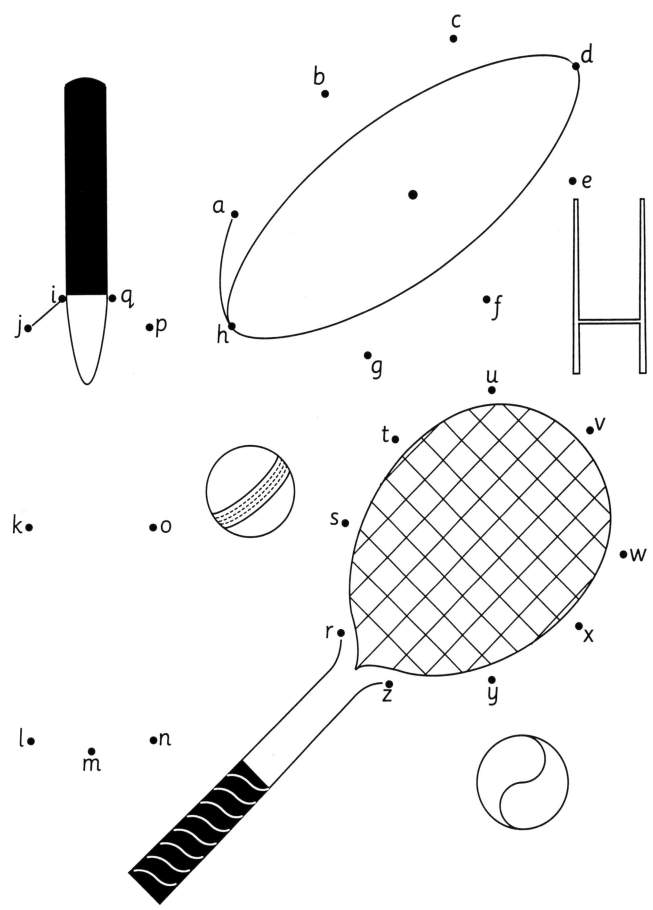

Developing Literacy Skills (4-5 years) © EJP and DCP

Name _____

## Write the missing letters.

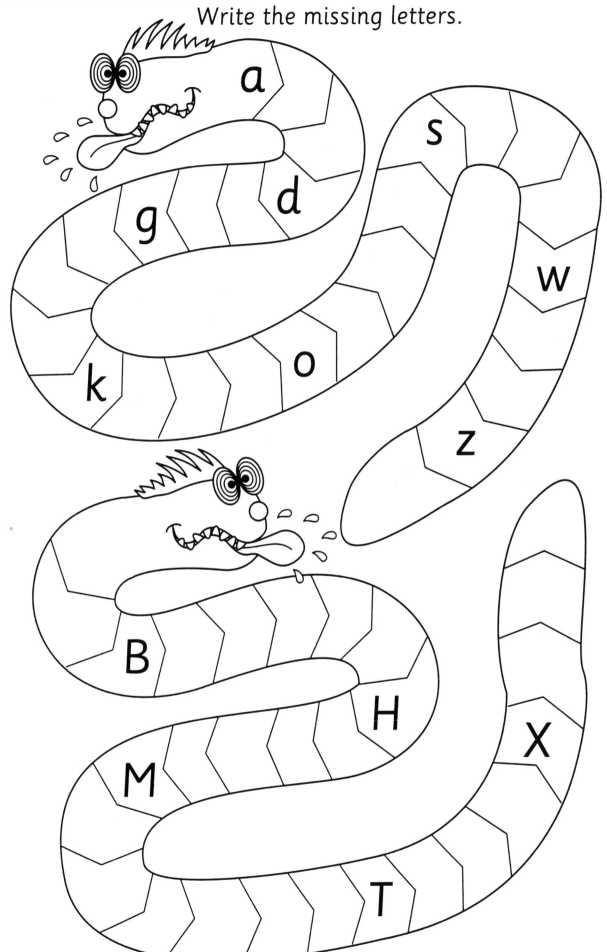

Name _____

## Draw and colour the path of the frog.

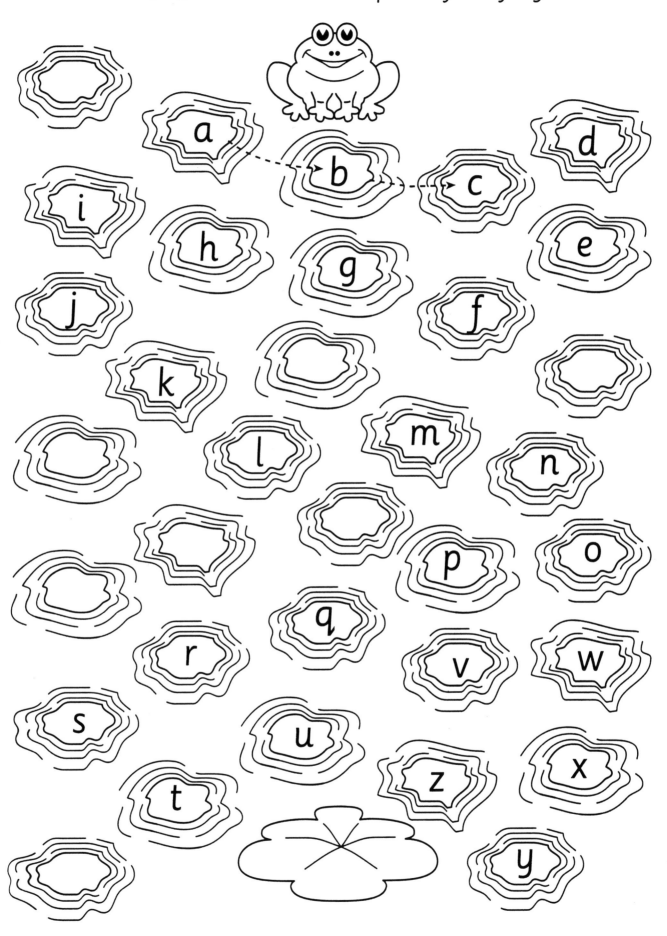

Name _____

## Draw lines to join the pairs of letters.

 a         D

 b         A

c         B

d         F

 e         C

 f         E

Name _____

## Draw lines to join the pairs of letters.

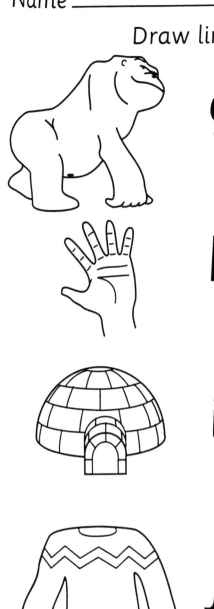

g

l

h

G

i

J

j

L

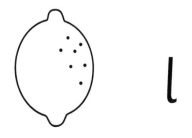

k

H

l

K

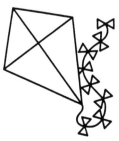

Letter pairs 47

Name _____

## Draw lines to join the pairs of letters.

m          M

n          O

o          N

p          R

q          Q

r          P

Name _____

## Draw lines to join the pairs of letters.

 s

 T

 t

 S

 u

 Y

v

 Z

 w

 U

 x

 V

 y

W

z

X

Developing Literacy Skills (4-5 years) © EJP and DCP

Letter pairs 49

Name _____

## Write the letter partners. ( A a )

A__    B__    C__    D__

E__    F__    G__    H__

I__    J__    K__    L__

M__    N__    O__    P__

Q__    R__    S__    T__

U__    V__    W__    X__

Y__    Z__

Name _____

Write the letter partners. ( a A )

a __        b __        c __        d __

e __        f __        g __        h __

i __        j __        k __        l __

m __        n __        o __        p __

q __        r __        s __        t __

u __        v __        w __        x __

y __        z __

Cut along the dotted lines.

| Alphabet Dominoes | Z | a | A | b |
| B | c | C | d | D | e |
| E | f | F | g | G | h |
| H | i | I | j | J | k |
| K | l | L | m | M | n |
| N | o | O | p | P | q |
| Q | r | R | s | S | t |
| T | u | U | v | V | w |
| W | x | X | y | Y | z |

Cut along the dotted lines.

| Alphabet Cards | a | b |
|---|---|---|
| c | d | e |
| f | g | h |
| i | j | k |
| l | m | n |
| o | p | q |
| r | s | t |
| u | v | w |
| x | y | z |

Developing Literacy Skills (4-5 years) © EJP and DCP

Alphabet Cards 53

# Cut along the dotted lines.

Developing Literacy Skills (4-5 years) © EJP and DCP

Name _____

Write the first letters. Say the words. Choose from b c d f g.

☐ ee    ☐ lown    ☐ og    ☐ rog

☐ ate    ☐ arrot    ☐ ear    ☐ rab

☐ olphin    ☐ airy    ☐ ox    ☐ orilla

☐ at    ☐ at    ☐ rum

Name _____

Write the first letters. Say the words. Choose from h j k l m.

 \_\_at

 \_\_ouse

 \_\_ug

 \_\_ey

 \_\_adder

 \_\_ouse

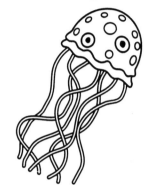 \_\_ellyfish

 \_\_ing

 \_\_emon

 \_\_an

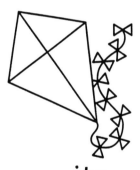 \_\_ite

 \_\_orse

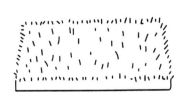 \_\_at

 \_\_adybird

 \_\_am

Name _____

Write the first letters. Say the words. Choose from n p q r s.

 \_\_nail

 \_\_irate

 \_\_ueen

 \_\_ail

 \_\_arrot

 \_\_et

 \_\_uilt

 \_\_anda

 \_\_uestion

 \_\_un

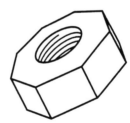 \_\_ut

 \_\_ock

 \_\_ing

 \_\_nake

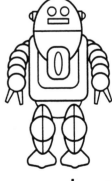 \_\_obot

Developing Literacy Skills (4-5 years) © EJP and DCP

Name _____

Write the first letters. Say the words. Choose from t v w x y z.

__ase          __ent          __atch          __- ray

__acht          __able          __ebra          __est

__eb          __ap          __an          __ig-zag

__indow          __o-yo

__awn

Name _____

Write the first letters. Say the words. Choose from a e i o u.

 __pple

 __nk

 __mbrella

 __range

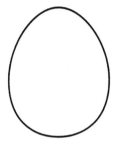 __gg

 __dder

 __nt

 __ctopus

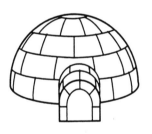 __gloo

 __lephant

 __ndian

 __ar

 __xe

 __nder

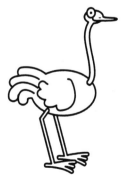 __strich

Developing Literacy Skills (4-5 years) © EJP and DCP

First Sounds 59

# Sound bingo cards

Cut out the three bingo cards.
Cross (X) a picture when you can match it to the sound of a letter.
The winner is the one with the most Xs.

# Sound bingo cards

Cut out the three bingo cards.
Cross (X) a picture when you can match it to the sound of a letter.
The winner is the one with the most Xs.

Name _____

Write b or d beside the pictures. Say the words.

☐ ee          ☐ olphin          ☐ onkey

☐ oll          ☐ ell             ☐ oat

☐ og          ☐ read            ☐ inosaur

☐ rain         ☐ ragon          ☐ in

☐ uck          ☐ at             ☐ one

Name _____

Write m or n beside the pictures. Say the words.

☐ oon

☐ ail

☐ ouse

☐ est

☐ onkey

☐ et

☐ op

☐ ermaid

☐ eedle

☐ ose

☐ ewspaper

DAILY PAPER

☐ ug

Name _____

Write the letters to finish the words. Say the words.

___at     ___at     ___at     ___at

___en     ___en     ___en     ___en

___in     ___in     ___in     ___in

___ot     ___ot     ___ot     ___ot

___un     ___un     ___un     ___un

Name _____

# Rhyming words.

Say the words. Cross out the pictures that do not rhyme.

| moon | spoon | wig | balloon |

| bee | tree | three | book |

| dog | frog | house | log |

| vest | top | mop | hop |

Write a word that rhymes with

bat _____        pen _____

fox _____        hut _____

Name _____

Write the missing middle letters. Choose from a e i o u.
Say the words.

f __ n

w __ g

b __ s

h __ t

p __ n

z __ p

l __ g

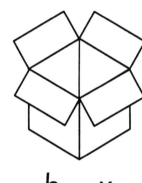
b __ x

t __ p

j __ g

t __ p

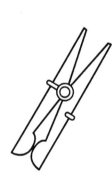
p __ g

s __ n

d __ g

p __ g

c __ t

Name _____

Complete the words and say them.

**ch**

___ain

___icken

___in

___ips

___eese

**sh**

___op

___ell

___ip

___eep

___oe

**th**

___roat

___imble

3 ___ree

___umb

___istle

Name _____

Complete the words and say them.
Choose from ch, sh, th.

_ _urch

fea_ _er

fi_ _

mo_ _

_ _air

_ _imble

_ _ark

_ _oe

_ _ick

wit_ _

Name _____

## Draw lines to match the opposites.

happy

asleep

awake

sad

hot

dirty

wet

cold

clean

dry

Name _____

Say the words. Find the letters missing from these signs.

 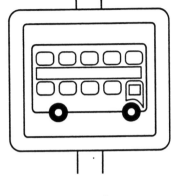 

_ar _ark          sch_ _ _l _us          _icycle tr_ck

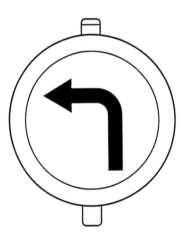 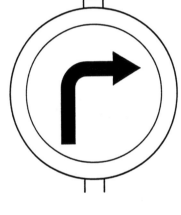 

_urn _eft          _urn _ight          _oo

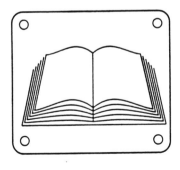  

_ook _orner          _rt _upboard          _oats

Name _____

## The Picnic

Find the missing words. Choose from.

| bus | asleep | ducks | picnic | cakes | sheep |
|-----|--------|-------|--------|-------|-------|

Henry and his mother went for a _____ in the country.

They saw _____ in a field.

They ate sandwiches and _____ .

Henry's mother fell _____ .

Henry fed the _____ in the pond.

Then they caught the _____ home.

Draw and colour a picture about a special day out that you enjoyed.

# Humpty Dumpty

Say the nursery rhyme then cut out the pictures and put them in the correct order.
Colour the pictures.

The King's men could have tried to mend Humpty with gl ——— and brown
p _____.

They could have used str ————.

Can you suggest any other ways they have tried to help?

# Little Miss Muffett

Say the nursery rhyme then cut out the pictures and put them in the correct order.
Colour the pictures.

Think of another ending for this nursery rhyme.

# Jack and Jill

Say the nursery rhyme then cut out the pictures and put them in the correct order.
Colour the pictures.

Think of another ending for this nursery rhyme.

# Henry's Day

Cut out the pictures and captions and place them in the correct order.

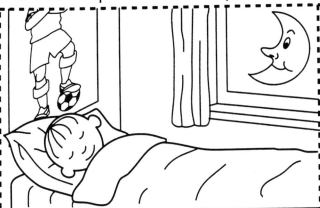

Henry sleeps in a room at the top of the house. He can see the moon through the window.

After breakfast, Henry waits for the school bus.

Henry plays with his friends at school.

Henry dresses quickly.

Then Henry has breakfast.

His mother wakes him early in the morning.

Draw 2 pictures to show two things you do in a day.
Write what you are doing underneath the pictures.

Name _____

## Santa's Presents

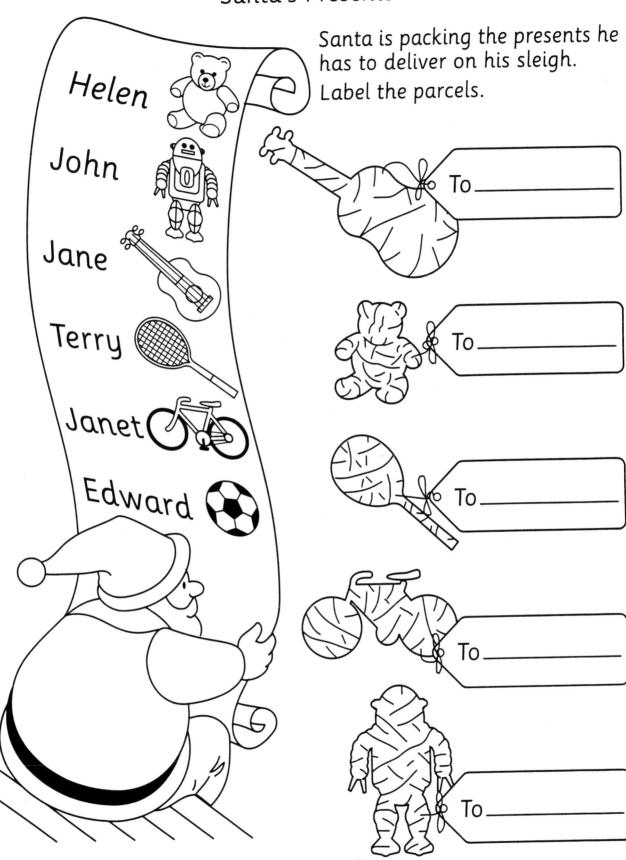

Helen

John

Jane

Terry

Janet

Edward

Santa is packing the presents he has to deliver on his sleigh.
Label the parcels.

To _____

To _____

To _____

To _____

To _____

Which present has Santa forgotten to wrap?
Draw and label this present when it has been wrapped.
What present would you like to have for your birthday?

Developing Literacy Skills (4-5 years) © EJP and DCP

Santa's Presents 76

# Goldilocks and the Three Bears

Daddy Bear

Mummy Bear

Baby Bear

Goldlilocks

Once upon a time there were three bears, Daddy Bear, Mummy Bear and Baby Bear. They lived in a small cottage in a forest.  was big with a deep voice.  was a smaller bear with a quiet voice and  was a very small bear with a squeaky voice.

One morning  made some porridge. He poured it into three bowls. There was a big  for Daddy Bear, a smaller  for Mummy Bear and a very small  for Baby Bear. The porridge was too hot and Daddy Bear suggested they should go for a walk while the porridge cooled.

 was also walking in the forest. When she came to the she knocked on the door but there was no answer. She opened the door and walked in. She could smell the porridge and remembered she had not had breakfast. She felt hungry.

saw three bowls of porridge on the table. She tasted the porridge in the big but It was too hot. She tasted the porridge in the medium-sized but it was too cold. Then she tasted the porridge in the small . It was just right and she ate it all up.

Suddenly, felt tired and she climbed up the stairs to find the bedroom. She tried the big . It was too hard. She tried the medium-sized . It was too soft. Then she tried the small . It was just right. She lay down and went to sleep. Soon the three bears returned from their walk. They sat at the table to eat their porridge. Daddy Bear sat in the big . Mummy Bear sat in the medium-sized and Baby Bear sat in the small .

'Who's been eating my porridge?' said in his deep voice.

'Who's been eating my porridge?' said in her quiet voice.

'Who's been eating my porridge?' said in his squeaky voice. 'And who's eaten it all up?' Baby Bear started to cry.

The Bears were feeling tired after their walk and climbed the stairs to the bedrooms.

'Who's been sleeping in my bed?' said Daddy Bear.

Who's been sleeping in my bed?' said Mummy Bear.

'Who is this, sleeping in my bed?' said Baby Bear.

Mummy Bear shook and woke her up. Goldilocks was so frightened she ran out of the and home as fast as she could.

Name _____

Draw a path for Goldilocks to follow through the forest to the
cottage where the three bears live.

Who sits in these chairs?

_____ _____ _____

Who sleeps in these beds?

 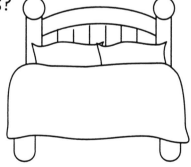 

_____ _____ _____

Name _____

Say what is happening in the pictures.
Cut out the captions and paste them under the correct pictures.

Name _____

# What happened ?

Pretend you are Goldilocks. Tell a friend about your adventure in the forest. Begin 'When I was walking in the forest...
Draw pictures of the cottage and the bears.

Don't forget to say
- what the forest was like,
- how you came upon the cottage,
- the door was open,
- what you found inside,
- what you did,
- why you went upstairs,
- how the adventure ended.

Pretend you are Baby Bear. Tell the story about the visit of the blonde girl to your cottage.

Don't forget to say
- Daddy Bear made porridge which was too hot,
- you all went for a walk in the forest leaving the porridge to cool,
- you came back to eat your porridge,
- what you found had happened while you were out,
- what had happened to your porridge,
- what you found when you went upstairs,
- how the story ended.

Pretend you are a detective sent to investigate the break-in at the cottage. Investigate

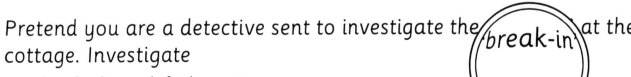

- why the bears left the cottage,
- why the door was left open,
- what they found when they returned to their cottage,
- what happened in the cottage while they were away.
- were any clues left?.

Find out if the culprit is 'known' to the police. Suggest how the crime might be solved.

# The Tortoise and The Hare

Tortoise

Hare

Cat

Hare was very proud of how fast he could run and how far he could jump.

Sometimes he ran around Tortoise just for fun.

'Look how fast I can run,'  shouted.  took no

notice but just kept going.

One day,  said, 'Let's have a race.'

'No thank you,' said  'I'm too busy.'

'You're afraid,' said Hare. 'You know how fast I can run. I dare you.'

He ran around Tortoise.

Tortoise yawned. Hare was a silly fellow, running about going nowhere.

'Very well,' said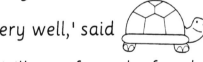

'We'll race from the farmhouse , up the hill and down to

the church,' said Hare.

'Alright,' said Tortoise.

'  can blow the whistle and be the referee,' said Hare.

Next day, Cat drew a starting line on the ground. Hare stood there

impatiently. 'Hurry up Tortoise,' he said, 'or the race will be over before

you've started.' He laughed at his joke.

When Tortoise reached the starting line, blew the whistle.

Hare was off in a flash. He passed a flock of watching the

race. He went to visit in the field. On the way he passed the

farmer on his . Next he ran over a bridge across a stream and

jumped over a gate. Then he stopped to speak to Mrs. and her

swimming in a pond. It was very hot and all this running

had made Hare tired. 'I may have a short nap,' he said. Tortoise will

never catch me.' He stretched out on a grassy bank and was soon

fast .

Slowly, Tortoise crawled up the hill, past the who cheered

him on, past and Mrs. with her family of .

He passed , softly snoring. Several

waved their tails as he passed them.

Just as Tortoise had nearly reached the Hare woke up. There

was no sign of so went back to sleep. It was quite

cool when Hare woke next. He started to run again just to keep warm.

He passed several and wondered why they

were laughing. It was then that he saw at , just

about to cross the finishing line. ran as fast as he could but

he could not catch Tortoise.

had lost the race and had won.

Name _____

# The Tortoise and the Hare Race

Use a red crayon to show where Tortoise went.
Use a blue crayon to show where Hare went.

start

finish

Who travelled furthest? Tortoise or Hare? _____

Who is the faster runner? _____ Who won the race? _____

Why did he win? _____

Name _____

# Be a reporter

Pretend you are a reporter for your local television station and give a commentary on the Great Hare and Tortoise Race.

Say what is happening as you watch the race.

Don't forget to interview Hare, Tortoise, Cat and spectators before and after the race.

Pretend you are a journalist for a local paper. Write about the Great Hare and Tortoise Race. Don't forget to say who was in it and who won it.

Draw pictures as well.

Pretend you are Hare. Explain why you lost.

Begin 'I was unlucky …

Pretend you are Tortoise. Explain why you raced against Hare and how you won.

Begin 'Hare is my best friend and one day he …

Pretend you are Cat. Explain how you started the race, what happened and how the race ended. Say if you think the race was fair.

Pretend to be Mrs Duck or one of the cows watching the race. Say what you think of the race and the animals who took part in it.

# Panda's New Coat

Cut out the pictures and captions and paste them in the correct order.

Panda goes to the shop with his mother.

The third coat is just r_ _ _ _

The first coat is too b_ _

Panda admires himself in the mirror.

Panda's coat is old and torn.

The second coat is too s_ _ _ _ _

## Films and Posters

Cut out the titles and paste them on the correct posters.

*Sleeping Beauty*
THE HAUNTED CASTLE
Canoeing down the Amazon
*The Adventures of Felix, the Cat*

Name _____

## Special Books

John buys these books. Match the covers and the pages.

John's mother likes gardening.

John's brother likes to sail on ships.

John's uncle likes travelling abroad.

John was given a puppy for his birthday.

Who will he give the books to?

What is your favourite book?

Draw a cover for it

# The National Literacy Strategy
## Sight Words
## Flash Cards.

| | |
|:---:|:---:|
| I | at |
| up | for |
| look | he |
| we | is |
| like | said |
| and | go |
| on | you |

Developing Literacy Skills (4-5 years) © EJP and DCP

| | |
|---|---|
| are | cat |
| this | to |
| going | come |
| they | day |
| away | the |
| play | dog |
| a | big |
| am | my |

| | |
|---|---|
| mum | of |
| no | me |
| dad | she |
| all | see |
| get | it |
| in | yes |
| went | can |
| was | |

# TEACHERS' NOTES

This book is planned to help children begin to understand pictorial and written material. It starts with reading pictures, introducing the concept that marks on a page have meaning. As their observational skills develop, the shapes and sounds of letters are introduced leading to the written word in context and stories. There are links with *Desirable Outcomes for Children's Learning* and the requirements of the *National Curriculum for Key Stage 1.*

## LITERACY HOUR

The Literacy Hour is based on the work done by the *National Literacy Strategy.* In the hour, children work at the comprehension and understanding of text and composition with activities at sentence level (grammar and punctuation) and at word level (vocabulary and spelling).

## SPEAKING

Children begin to acquire language in their parents' arms. They learn to associate the human voice with the sensations of food, warmth and comfort. At first, language is a a means to an end and it is used by the young child to attract attention and to indicate what he or she wants: food, milk, love, warmth and so on. Very young children build up a store of the names of different objects and nouns and verbs (the content words) are used first because they contain most meaning. The functional words: articles, prepositions, conjunctions come next and finally syntax and grammar (masculine and feminine, singulars and plurals, number and colour) come last. Talking to babies and young children is very important. They listen and instinctively learn. By the age of four or five, most children can be understood, they have basic (spoken) language acquisition. They can use most of the 44 or so phonemes of English and have a vocabulary of more than 3,000 words. They have started to master the rules leading to the formation of sentences and have begun to string several together. In school the children will become familiar with such words as listen, question, discuss, word, letter and sound.

Children at this age enjoy taking part in conversations, they are able to express their needs and feelings and ask questions. They enjoy reciting rhymes, poems, jingles, songs and retelling stories. The familiarity of their favourite stories creates comfort and security (especially at bedtime) with anticipation and excitement but no unpleasant surprises.

Most children can say the common vowels and consonants of spoken English. They may alternate between similar sounds, e.g. *th-* as in thistle may becom *f-* . Such characteristics usually disappear naturally.

By now, children have acquired an impressive grasp of grammar. This is not the rules of formal English but rather the ability to put words into utterances which can be understood. Their speech will show the characteristics expected of their efforts to pick up and use the sometimes eccentric rules of English. Thus, a child may use *sitted* (sat) and *thinked* (thought). It may not be sensible to correct these 'errors' and interrupt the child's thoughts. The characteristics of a child's speech shows his or her progress.

## LISTENING

It is important that children learn to sit and listen. This is best done by giving them reasons to do so. Introduce a variety of stories, poems and nursery rhymes, give the children the opportunity to talk to the class. Encourage them to learn to work in groups and learn to listen to each other. Children need experience in conversation adapted to their level and also in listening to more adult speech. Questions should be open-ended so that there is room for their input. Remember that it is generally not helpful to insist on a child correcting and repeating an utterance which is understandable but not absolutely grammatically correct. Children should have the opportunity to talk about and listen to the experiences of each other, listen to music, take part in role play and retell stories.

## LANGUAGE AND LITERACY

Children are expected to
>   listen carefully and talk about their experiences.
>   use a developing vocabulary.
>   respond to stories, songs, rhymes and poems.

make up their own stories.

enjoy books and handle them carefully.

understand that words and pictures carry meaning.

understand that, in English, print is read from left to right and from top to bottom.

link sounds with words and letters.

recognise their own names and some familiar words.

know the alphabet and write their names correctly.

# EARLY READING SKILLS

## SKILLS IN READING

These involve:

Learning to read pictures and to sequence several pictures.

Learning the shapes of the letters.

Learning the sounds of letters and groups of letters.

Learning the shapes of familiar words so that they can be recognised.

Practice in recognising/reading different letters.

Learning to read and know the sounds of the alphabet.

Learning to write his or her own name (using capital letters as appropriate).

Learning that reading is from left to right.

Learning that the written word is read from left to right.

Practice and the development of motor and co-ordination skills.

Development of an awareness of the purpose of reading.

Learning to use reading and writing for different purposes, e.g. make a birthday card, keep a diary, compile a spelling list.

Learning to sequence, remember and develop a story.

## WORDS

Understanding that words can be separated into speech sounds or phonemes does not usually develop until the children have started to read. However, children soon become interested in the way in which words or syllables can be separated into initial sounds and rhymes* They are fascinated with nursery rhymes, jingles and tongue twisters. They will become familiar with words in their environment such as road signs, the names of foods in shops and so on. Children acquire a sight vocabulary by using words in context.

## THE ALPHABET

Children need to be able to relate print to the sounds made by letters. It is important they learn the function of the letters and that one letter, especially a vowel, may represent several sounds. Young children find the alphabet difficult. Lower case letters give words distinctive shapes while capital letters do not. The letters need to be reinforced by all the methods you know. Let the children colour the drawings in the photocopiable masters and say the letters and words. The sheets can be photocopied, enlarged or laminated. Let the children cut out the letters and paste them in their books.

## LETTER SOUNDS

Children need to know

1. the sounds that individual letters stand for.
2. the sounds made by the most common combination of letters, e.g. sh, ch, th.
3. that the same combination of letters usually produces the same sound in different words, e.g. cat, bat, mat.
4. that common words are recognised as a whole, e.g. the, and.
5. Children may learn the names of letters before they know their sounds, e.g. bee and they have to learn the link between name and sound.

Learning the sounds of letters is not easy and can seem tedious.

1. Select a sound for the day and concentrate on it.
2. Have a sound table or box for objects beginning with a particular letter/sound.
3. Make lists or draw pictures containing words beginning with the same letter.
4. Make a list of letters that are often seen e.g. M (MacDonald's), P O (Post Office)

*The onset is the part of the word or syllable that comes before the vowel sound. The rime is the part of the word or syllable that includes the vowel and the following consonant sound. For example, in drawing, *dr* and *w* are onsets and *a* and *ing* are rimes ). Children who recognise onset-rime units are often better readers.

There are many games that help.

1. **I Spy.** Use the letter sounds not the names of the letters, e.g. I spy something beginning with ah.
2. **Letter Table.** Each week choose one letter and collect objects and pictures that begin with this letter. Label and display them on a table or on the wall.
3. **Letter trays.** Label two trays with different letters. Prepare a collection of items starting with one or other of the letters. The children then sort the items into the correct tray.
4. **Letter scrap book.** A different letter is written on each page and children collect pictures and words that start with each letter and paste them in the book. They my also like to add their own drawings.
5. **Tongue twisters.** These help children to concentrate on particular sounds, e.g. Peter Piper picked a peck of pickled pepper.

**Checklist for Sounds**

| | | | | | | | | |
|---|---|---|---|---|---|---|---|---|
| **ah** | is for | apple | **juh** | is for | jelly | **suh** | is for | sun |
| **buh** | is for | ball | **kuh** | is for | kitten | **tuh** | is for | top |
| **cuh** | is for | cat | **luh** | is for | ladybird | **uh** | is for | umbrella |
| **duh** | is for | dog | **muh** | is for | mother | **vuh** | is for | van |
| **eh** | is for | egg | **nuh** | is for | nut | **wuh** | is for | witch |
| **fuh** | is for | fish | **oh** | is for | orange | **x** | is for | x-ray |
| **guh** | is for | goat | **puh** | is for | penguin | **yuh** | is for | yoyo |
| **huh** | is for | house | **qwuh** | is for | queen | **zuh** | is for | zebra |
| **ih** | is for | ink | **ruh** | is for | rat | | | |

## READING ACTIVITIES

Reading is one of the most important skills acquired by children. We read for information and very importantly, for pleasure. Reading should be presented as something to be enjoyed.

**'Reading' pictures.** This leads to an understanding that drawings, pictures, that is material on a page, has meaning. Children begin to identify this material with their surroundings and what happens to them. Realising that a flat drawing represents a soft, fat, cuddly toy is a remarkable achievement. [Most of us have been driven to distraction constructing the simplest object using diagrams in an instruction sheet!] Situations pictures such as 'in the park' can be discussed and children should be able to suggest what is happening and tell about their own experiences.

Where necessary prompt with, for example, 'What/who is that? What are they doing?' 'Where are they?' and when appropriate, 'What do you think will happen next?'

**Sequencing and matching.** These skills are important as a basis for the recognition of groups of letters and words. Begin with simple pictures and ask what will happen next. Drawings of familiar stories and nursery rhymes shown first in sequence and then out of order are useful.

**Telling stories.** Children like to be told stories. This widens their experiences and imagination beyond their own surroundings. They should be encouraged to tell stories themselves. This develops vocabulary, imagination and memory.

**Drawing** This helps children understand and relate to material on the page as well as developing motor skills. Always encourage children to colour their work. Ask them to tell you what their picture is about.

**Predicting.** Saying what will happen next helps children think about the picture in front of them and develops imagination.

**Matching.** Finding out what is the same or different between two or more pictures develops observation skills. Reading depends on instant recognition of letters and groups of letters that are the same or different.

**Focusing on detail.** Reading depends on detailed recognition. Paying attention to details around them, in pictures and in books helps to develop these skills. When learning to write, children are helped to learn the shapes of letters by copying them. Exercises in letter recognition - those that are the same and the 'odd letter out' are helpful.

Children use a variety of clues and skills to read. Pictures are very important and if the story is familiar, there may well be some intelligent guessing. It is important to encourage the children to make progress and not become lost in a sea of print. Encourage children to sit comfortably and to sit upright.

## METHODS USED TO TEACH READING

**Phonic method.** This aims to build up an understanding of how our alphabet works, of the letters and the sounds they represent. It enables children to say words they do not know.

**Look and say.** This aims to teach children a growing sight vocabulary of complete words that they can recognise and

say at once. It relies on repetition and requires a scheme with a controlled vocabulary.

**'Real' books/whole language.** This approach aims to absorb children's attention by using exciting stories and natural language so the children begin to focus on, predict and remember the words they see. The stories selected do not necessarily come from a particular reading scheme.

## HOW A BOOK WORKS.
Children need to know
how to hold a book.
how the front of a book is different from the inside.
that we keep the book still and turn the pages. (Encourage the child to turn the pages when you read).
that the pictures are full of interesting information.
that a story is exciting to listen to.

Shared reading involves groups of children reading large books with enlarged text. Children may be asked to identify key words in the text, to find words beginning with a particular letter or containing particular letters and simple cloze tests in which a word is covered and the children make an informed guess.

## READING CORNER
When children start to take an interest in books or other reading material, it is important that there is a quiet place where they can look at books or read in peace. This may be a favourite chair or in nursery it may be a corner with chairs, stools, several large cushions, a desk and a mat.

# EARLY WRITING SKILLS

## PRE-WRITING SKILLS
Sequencing and matching are important as a basis for writing later on. For example, adding tails to animals, colouring and tracing activities, cutting and pasting are part of the early development of these important skills. Teach the children to hold crayons and pencils 'properly'.

**Scribbling.** A child's first efforts look like random marks on a surface. Encourage the use of pens, pencils and crayons. Avoid 'disasters' by ensuring that the children learn where they can work and have comfortable surroundings. This is play and should be enjoyed.

**Tracking.** Children should be taught to track vertically and horizontally.

**Letter development.** Letters emerge from the scribbling. Often, children use just one letter to represent a word. Show that in English, writing starts at the top left hand corner of a page and proceeds from left to right and down the page. Children will see writing all around them. When they are read to, they begin to realise that written words have meaning. They soon have favourite stories that they want read again and again.

**Copying.** Children are helped to learn the shapes of letters by copying them. This may be by writing over the top of existing letters or copying. Show the children how to form letters correctly.

**Independent writing.** When children begin to remember words and spelling develops, they start to write simple sentences or phrases.

Some children are more comfortable using their left hand. In general, allow a child to use which hand he/she prefers.

## SPELLING
Children may represent words by pictures or combinations of letters that seem to be random. Later, children begin to form shapes for letters although these may vary in direction and size. Similarly, such letters as *b* and *d, f* and *t, p* and *q* may be interchanged. By the end of their time in the reception class, most children will understand the one-to-one relationship between a written word and its spoken partner. Although correct spelling may still have far to go, the children should be able to write down and read back simple statements.

## WORD LEVEL ACTIVITIES
These provide a link between the reading of whole texts and the teaching of letter-sound relationships.
1. **Games and recitations** of rhyming, alliteratiave and onomatopoeic songs, stories and poems
2. **I spy.** Adapt games in which children say as many words as they can remember with the same beginnings or endings.
3. **Odd one out.** This involves recognising a word that differs from the others in a series.
4. **Alphabet frieze.** Let the children make a large alphabet frieze.

5. **Use alphabets** of names, animals and so on.
6. **Make vocabulary lists**.

## HANDWRITING

Children should examine the differences and similarities between letters. They should track letters and trace do-to-dot patterns. Tracing letters in sand or in the air is also helpful.

## ENCOURAGING WRITING AND COPYING

Encourage children to contribute to different activities.
1. **Family words.** Make large cards for the children and their families so that the names are special for them.
2. **Museum corner and labels.** Children should bring items that are special to them. The objects are then labelled and displayed. This can have a changing theme every week.
3. **Special occasion cards.** Children can design and write cards, e.g. for birthdays, invitations,Christmas and other religious festivals.
4. **Lists.** There are always plenty of lists to compile, e.g. shopping lists, invitations, birthdays, favourite foods, packing lists …
5. **Free play and role play.**
    Shopping lists, waiter writing down what the diner wants to eat, doctor writing prescriptions, secretary or receptionist making appointments, booking into a hotel, cookery recipes, menus, notices, advertisements…
6. **Keeping a diary** exercises a variety of skills: retelling stories and experiences, vocabulary, writing as well as the concepts of days and dates.

## MOTOR SKILLS

The development of writing requires considerable skill and hand control. [Remember what it felt like when you first learned to ride a bike, drive a car, learned to type or tried to control the mouse of a computer.]
1. Making things using Plasticine, clay or Play-Doh.
2. Jigsaws. Make sure that they are suitable for the age and ability of the children. Putting a jigsaw together involves shape, size, making things fit and careful observation.
3. Building and construction toys such as bricks.
4. Threading beads.
5. Cutting and pasting.
6. Painting and colouring drawings.
7. Tracing drawings.
8. Joining the dots and maze puzzles.
9. Tracking along 'roads and paths' from left to right.
10. Copying and drawing over large versions of writing patterns.

# ACTIVITIES

**Page 5**     **Me.** It is important that children develop their own identity, understand who they are.

**Pages 6 - 7**  **Reading pictures.** This helps develop observational skills and introduces the concepts that shapes and outlines on paper have meaning. Ask what the children can see and what is happening in the pictures. This develops vocabulary and imagination. Where possible help the children relate the pictures to their own experiences. Extend the activity by encouraging the children to colour the pictures and then draw their own. Ask them to comment on what they have drawn.

**Pages 8 - 10**  **Matching.** Reading requires instant matching of letters into word patterns. Matching drawings helps develop the observational skills needed. Be sure the children can name the items and encourage them to colour the pictures. Page 9 involves spotting the 'odd one out'.

**Page 11 - 13**  **Sequencing.** Drawings are used to help the children acquire the concepts of sequence and order. Ask the children to comment on each drawing and, if possible, explain their choice of drawings.

**Page 14 - 15**  **Sequencing.** Each pair of drawings involves two events that can occur in one order only e.g the cake is whole before it is cut and here the eggs come before the chicks. This activity is harder than might appear and the children have to think carefully about what is happening in the pictures.

**Page 16**    **Sequencing.** Here the choice is between what is reasonable and what is apparently absurd or unlikely.

**Page 17 - 42 The alphabet.** Activities involve the names of letters, their shapes and the sounds they make. There are numerous drawings to help. Each sheet has work on the recognition, sound and formation of one letter.

**Page 43 - 45 The alphabet.** Puzzles based on the alphabet. These activities help with letter recognition, the sounds the letters make and the development of writing skills.

**Pages 46 - 51 Activities** based on letter recognition.

**Page 52**    **Alphabet dominoes** provide an amusing and interesting way of matching letters, both lower case and capitals. To make the dominoes last, paste them on to card before they are cut out.

**Pages 53 - 54 Alphabet cards.** These should be pasted on to card and cut out to be used in letter recognition and letter sounds activities, for example, match the picture cards with their first letters.

**Page 55 - 59 First letter sounds.** Practice in saying and writing the sounds at the beginning of a variety of words. The children also begin to recognise and read words in their context.

**Pages 60 - 61 Sound bingo sheets (cards).** These provide practice in matching sounds and words. Each child has a sheet. Show a letter and the children mark any picture on their sheets that begins with the letter. The winner is the one who marks all the pictures on his or her sheet. To make long lasting sheets, paste the sheets on thin card and laminate them.

**Pages 62 - 63 Words and pictures.** Activities to help distinguish between *b* and *d, m* and *n*. The children can make *b* or *d* or *m* or *n* pages in a spelling book.

**Pages 64 - 65 Rhyming words.** Extend these activities with more examples and by asking the children to say words that rhyme and make lists of words with just the first letter changing.

**Page 66**    **Vowels** Missing letters have to be found and the words should be said.

**Pages 67 - 68 ch, sh, th.** Activities involve these special groups of letters. The children's work can be made into ch, sh or th pages in spelling books. The children may make their own displays including drawings and words such as chips, ship, thimble and say tongue twisters such as *'She sells sea shells on the sea shore.'*

**Page 69**    **Opposites.** These pictures illustrate the meaning of some common opposites. The children may add their own examples.

**Page 70**    **Everyday signs.** It is important that children realise that signs have meanings and that they learn what they mean. Extend this with signs the children are likely to meet in and outside school.

**Page 71**    **Pictures and text.** These activities involve children in choosing the correct word to fit the text that goes with the pictures. Extend these activities by the children drawing pictures about their own signs and posters.

**Pages 72 - 74 Sequencing.** Ordering and colouring pictures about well known nursery rhymes relate pictures, their meaning and the spoken/written word. The familiarity of the material makes it all the more fun.

**Page 75**    **Sequencing.** Henry's Day requires the children to interpret a series of pictures into a connected story. Extend the activity by the children drawing pictures about their days.

**Page 76**    **Santa's presents.** This involves understanding a list and the recognition of shapes.

**Pages 77 - 78 Reading and pictures.** The use of pictures in the text enables the children to take part in the reading of the familiar story of *Goldilocks.*

**Pages 79 - 81 Puzzles and activities** on the story of *Goldilocks.* Page 79 requires children to work out the path for Goldilocks and to recognise items of different size. Page 80 involves arranging pictures in order to suit the order of events in a story. Page 81 is the basis for discussion of what has happened in the story and how the events can be discussed from different viewpoints.

**Pages 82 - 83** *The Tortoise and the Hare.* Again pictures in the text make it easier for the children to read.

**Pages 84 - 85 Puzzles and activities** on the story of *The Tortoise and the Hare.* The race requires the children to relate text to what happens on a map of the event. The children are also asked to consider the behaviour of the Tortoise and Hare and what effect this has on the result of the race.

**Page 86      Panda's coat.** Puzzle involving observation and deduction. Most children will have experience of clothes that do not fit them perfectly.

**Pages 87 - 88 Activities** linking text and pictures.

**Pages 89 - 91 Flash cards** from the National Literacy Strategy

# STORIES AND RHYMES

## STORIES
Aladdin
Beauty and the Beast
Beddgelert
Charlie and the Chocolate Factory
Cinderella
Goldilocks and the Three Bears
Gulliver's Travels
Hansel and Gretel
Jack and the Beanstalk
James and the Giant Peach
Little Red Riding Hood
Rumplestiltskin
Pinocchio
Puss in Boots
Rapunzel
Ricki Tikki Tavi
Robin Hood
Sleeping Beauty
Snow White
The Cat and the Fox
The Hare and the Tortoise
The Princess and the Pea
The Three Billy Goats Gruff
The Three Little Pigs
The Ugly Duckling
Thumbelina

## NURSERY RHYMES
As I was going to St Ives
Baa Baa Black Sheep
Ding Dong Dell
Georgie Porgie
Hey Diddle Diddle
Hickory, Dickory, Dock
Humpty Dumpty
Hush-a-Bye, Baby
Jack and Jill
Little Bo-Peep
Mary Had a Little Lamb
Monday's Child
Old King Cole
One, Two, Buckle My Shoe

Oh Dear, What Can the Matter Be?
Oh, the Brave Old Duke of York
Polly, Put the Kettle On
Pop Goes the Weasel
Sing a Song of Sixpence
The First Day of Christmas
The North Wind Does Blow
There was a Crooked Man
There was an Old Woman Who Lived in a Shoe
Three Blind Mice
Twinkle, Twinkle, Little Star

## ACTION RHYMES
Here We Go Looby Loo
Here We Go Round the Mulberry Bush
Old Macdonald Had a Farm
One, Two, Buckle My Shoe
One, Two, Three, Four, Five,
        Once I Caught a Fish Alive
One, Two, Three, Four, Mary at the Cottage Door
Oranges and Lemons
Ring-a-Ring a'Roses
Ten Green Bottles
The Farmer's in His Den
This is the Way We Wash Our Face
Two Little Dicky Birds

## FINGER PLAY RHYMES
Church and Steeple
Five Fat Gentlemen
Five Little Soldiers
Here's the Lady's Knives and Forks
I Am a Teapot
Peter Hammers with One Hammer
Incy Wincy Spider
Ten Little Men
Two Little Dicky Birds

## TONGUE TWISTERS
Fuzzy Wuzzy Was a Bear
How Much Wood Would a Woodchuck Chuck
Peter Piper Picked a Peck of Pickled Pepper
She Sells Sea Shells on the Sea Shore

# DEVELOPING LITERACY SKILLS
## CHECKLIST

| √ | | √ | |
|---|---|---|---|
| | Development of observational skills | | Recognition of initial clusters and blends |
| | Developing listening skills | | Opposites |
| | Developing basic vocabulary | | Words in everyday use |
| | Matching objects | | Signs |
| | Sequencing a series of objects (2s) | | Sequencing pictures |
| | Sequencing a series of objects (3s) | | Sequencing events in stories |
| | 'Reading' pictures | | Lists |
| | Picture order | | Reading stories |
| | Prediction | | Retelling a story |
| | Recognition of the sounds of letters | | Matching pictures and captions |
| | Recognition of the shapes of letters | | Reading a map |
| | The alphabet | | Writing a report |
| | Letters and sounds | | Structure of a book |
| | Join the dots | | Importance of the cover of a book |
| | Capital letters and alphabet partners | | Design of posters |
| | Rhyming words | | Interpretation of posters |
| | Vowels | | |

NATIONAL CURRICULUM

MASTER FILE

# MASTER FILES

published by
Domino Books (Wales) Ltd.

## AN ESTABLISHED SERIES
## prepared by experienced teachers

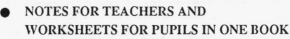

- NOTES FOR TEACHERS AND WORKSHEETS FOR PUPILS IN ONE BOOK

- COMPREHENSIVE NATIONAL CURRICULUM COVERAGE

- THERE IS NO NEED TO BUY ADDITIONAL MATERIAL

- ALL THE MATERIAL IS PHOTOCOPIABLE

- EXCELLENT VALUE

- SAVES YOU TIME AND MONEY

- VISUALLY STIMULATING

- BOOKS SPECIFICALLY DESIGNED FOR THE KEY STAGE YOU TEACH

- FULL OF TEACHING STRATEGIES AND IDEAS

- READY-TO-USE LESSONS

- FLEXIBLE RESOURCES FOR USE BY THE WHOLE CLASS, BY GROUPS OR BY INDIVIDUAL PUPILS

- TRIED AND TESTED MATERIALS

- PHOTOCOPIABLE SHEETS TO USE AS THEY ARE OR TO REDUCE OR ENLARGE

- PHOTOCOPIABLE RECORD SHEETS FOR EACH PUPIL

- NEW TITLES PUBLISHED MONTHLY

## AVAILABLE FROM
**Domino Books (Wales) Ltd**
**P O Box 32, Swansea SA1 1FN**
**Tel. (01792) 459378  Fax. (01792) 466337**
**www.dominobooks.co.uk**
**email: sales@dominobooks.co.uk**

ORDER FORM OVERLEAF

# MASTER FILES
## ORDER FORM

**KEY STAGE 1 (Age 5 - 7)**      **KEY STAGE 2 (Age 7 - 11)**      **KEY STAGE 3 (Age 11 - 14)**

| Quantity | Title | ISBN | Price | Cost |
|---|---|---|---|---|
| | KS1 ENGLISH | 1 85772 111 X | £20.00 | £ |
| | KS1 MATHEMATICS | 1 85772 107 1 | £20.00 | £ |
| | KS1 MENTAL MATHEMATICS | 1 85772 154 3 | £20.00 | £ |
| | KS1 SCIENCE | 1 85772 108 X | £20.00 | £ |
| | KS1 HISTORY | 1 85772 112 8 | £20.00 | £ |
| | KS2 ENGLISH | 1 85772 085 7 | £20.00 | £ |
| | KS2 MATHEMATICS | 1 85772 086 5 | £20.00 | £ |
| | KS2 SCIENCE | 1 85772 087 3 | £20.00 | £ |
| | KS3 ENGLISH | 1 85772 127 6 | £20.00 | £ |
| | KS3 MATHEMATICS | 1 85772 126 8 | £20.00 | £ |
| | KS3 SCIENCE | 1 85772 128 4 | £20.00 | £ |
| **HISTORY** | | | | |
| | KS2 Invaders and Settlers, The Celts | 1 85772 067 9 | £15.95 | £ |
| | KS2 Invaders and Settlers, The Romans | 1 85772 070 9 | £15.95 | £ |
| | KS2 Invaders and Settlers, The Vikings | 1 85772 069 5 | £15.95 | £ |
| | KS2 Life in Tudor Times | 1 85772 076 8 | £15.95 | £ |
| | KS2/KS3 Victorian Britain | 1 85772 077 6 | £15.95 | £ |
| | KS2 - KS3 Second World War | 1 85772 121 7 | £20.00 | £ |
| **TOPICS** | | | | |
| | KS2/KS3 Castles | 1 85772 075 X | £15.95 | £ |
| | CHRISTMAS (AGES 5 - 12) | 1 85772 065 2 | £20.00 | £ |
| **NEW FOR EARLY YEARS** | | | | |
| | First Steps Basic Activities in the 3Rs | 1 85772 130 6 | £12.50 | £ |
| | First Steps Number and Counting | 1 85772 133 0 | £12.50 | £ |
| | First Steps Beginning to Read | 1 85772 138 1 | £12.50 | £ |
| | First Steps Beginning to Write | 1 85772 139 X | £12.50 | £ |
| | First Steps Beginning Mental Maths | 1 85772 142 X | £12.50 | £ |
| | First Steps Mental Maths, 5 - 6 years | 1 85772 143 8 | £12.50 | £ |
| | First Steps Mental Maths, 6 - 7 years | 1 85772 146 2 | £12.50 | £ |
| | First Steps Mental Maths, 7 - 8 years | 1 85772 147 0 | £12.50 | £ |
| | First Steps Mental Maths 8 - 9 years | 1 85772 148 9 | £12.50 | £ |
| | First Steps Developing Literacy Skills 4 - 5 years | 1 85772 151 9 | £12.50 | £ |
| | First Steps Developing Literacy Skills 5 - 6 years | 1 85772 152 7 | £12.50 | £ |
| | First Steps Developing Literacy Skills 6 - 7 years | 1 85772 153 5 | £12.50 | £ |
| | Reading and Comprehension 5 - 7 years, Book 1 | 1 85772 144 6 | £12.50 | £ |
| | Reading and Comprehension 5 - 7 years, Book 2 | 1 85772 145 4 | £12.50 | £ |
| | | | **Total** | £ |

**Name/Organisation/School**

**Address**

Post Code          Tel.

**Contact**          Signature

**Order Number**          Date

Available from **Blackwells, Foyles Bookshop, Waterstones, Welsh Books Council, WH Smith,** and all good booksellers or direct from

**DOMINO BOOKS (WALES) LTD, P O BOX 32, SWANSEA SA1 1 FN.**
Tel. 01792 459378   Fax. 01792 466337
www.dominobooks.co.uk    email:   sales@dominobooks.co.uk

All official orders must have an official requisition form attached (schools, educational establishments, LEAs, bookshops, libraries). Cheques with private orders please.